Just Like Me

D1369931

The Turnip

Grandpa planted
a turnip. It grew
bigger
and bigger
and bigger!

One day Grandpa
went to pull it up.
He pulled and he pulled,
but it wouldn't come up.

2

Grandpa called Grandma
to come and help him.
Out she came running.

So Grandma
pulled Grandpa,
and Grandpa
pulled the turnip.
They pulled
and they pulled,
but still it
wouldn't come up.

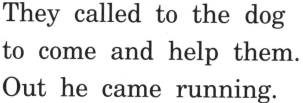

They called to the dog
to come and help them.
Out he came running.

3

The dog pulled Grandma,
Grandma pulled Grandpa,
and Grandpa pulled the turnip.
They pulled and they pulled,
but still it wouldn't come up.

They called to the cat
to come and help them.
Out she came running.

So the cat pulled the dog,
the dog pulled Grandma,
Grandma pulled Grandpa,
and Grandpa pulled
the turnip.

They pulled and they pulled,
but still it wouldn't come up.

They called to the
mouse to come
and help them.

Out she came
running.

5

So...the mouse pulled the cat,
the cat pulled the dog,
the dog pulled Grandma,
Grandma pulled Grandpa,
and Grandpa pulled the turnip.
They pulled
   and they **pulled**
      and they **pulled**.

And **up** came the turnip!

6

Then...Grandpa fell on Grandma,
Grandma fell on the dog,
the dog fell on the cat,
and the cat fell on the mouse.
And on top of them all
was the turnip!

But...they all had turnip to eat
that night.

7

And What Else?

Once upon a time
there was a little house.
And what else?
And this little house
had a door.

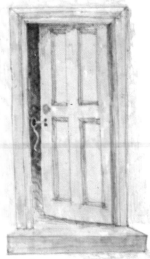

And what else?
And in this door
there was a key.
And what else?

And on this key
there was a string.
And what else?
And this string
was gnawed by a mouse.
And what else?
And this mouse
was chased by a cat.
And what else?
And this cat
was bitten by a dog.
And what else?
And this dog
was whacked by a stick.

And what else?
And this stick
was burned in a fire.
And what else?
And this fire
was put out by water.
And what else?
And this water
was drunk by an ox.
And what else?
And this ox was
followed by a butcher.
And what else?

And this butcher died...

And what else?
Before he died
this butcher followed an ox.
And what else?
And this ox
drank some water.
And what else?
And this water
put out a fire.
And what else?
And this fire
burned a stick.
And what else?

And this stick
whacked a dog.
And what else?
And this dog
bit a cat.
And what else?
And this cat
chased a mouse.
And what else?
And this mouse
gnawed a string.
And what else?
And this string
was on a key.

And what else?
And this key
was in a door.
And what else?
And this door
was in a little house.
And what else?
And this little house
had a bell.
And what else?
And...
well, well, well,
that's all
I'm going
to tell!

The Bear Went over the Mountain

The bear went over the mountain,
The bear went over the mountain,
The bear went over the mountain,
  To see what he could see.

He saw another mountain,
He saw another mountain,
He saw another mountain,
  And what do you think he did?

14

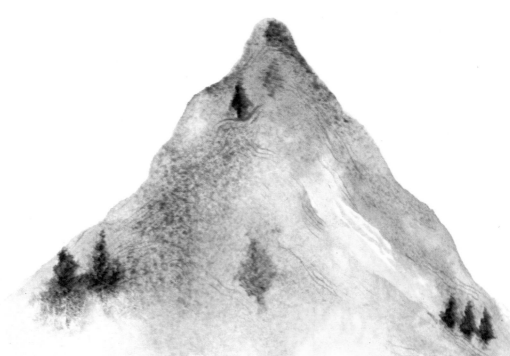

He climbed that other mountain,
He climbed that other mountain,
He climbed that other mountain,
   And what do you think he saw?

He saw another mountain,
He saw another mountain,
He saw another mountain,
   And what do you think he did?

The Greedy Old Fat Man

Once there was a greedy old fat man
who couldn't get enough to eat.

He got up one morning
and ate a pot of mush
and drank a barrel of milk.
But still he was hungry.
He went out of his house
and met a little boy.
The little boy says, "Old man,
what makes you so fat?"

Old man,
what makes
you so fat?

"I ate a pot of mush,
and I drank a barrel of milk,
and I'll eat you too
if I can catch you."

So he caught the little boy
and swallowed him down whole.
Then he went on
till he met
a little girl.

Old man
what
makes you
so fat?

The little girl says,
"Old man, what
makes you so fat?"

"I ate a pot of mush,
I drank a barrel of milk,
I ate a little boy, and I'll eat
you too if I can catch you."

So he caught the little girl
and swallowed her down whole.
Then he went on till he met
a little dog.

The little dog says, "Old man,
what makes you so fat?"

"I ate a pot of mush,
I drank a barrel of milk,
I ate a little boy,
I ate a little girl,
and I'll eat you too
if I can catch you."

So he caught the little dog
and swallowed her down whole.

Then he went on
till he met a little cat.

The little cat says, "Old man,
what makes you so fat?"

Me·ow
old man.
what makes
you so fat?

"I ate a pot of mush,
I drank a barrel of milk,
I ate a little boy,
I ate a little girl,
I ate a little dog,
and I'll eat you too
if I can catch you."

20

So he caught the little cat
and swallowed him down
whole. Then he went on
till he met a little fox.

The little fox says, "Old man,
what makes you so fat?"

"I ate a pot of mush,
I drank a barrel of milk,
I ate a little boy,
I ate a little girl,
I ate a little dog,
I ate a little cat,
and I'll eat you too
if I can catch you."

21

So he caught the little fox
and swallowed him down
whole. Then he went on
till he met a little rabbit.

The little rabbit says,
"Old man, what makes
you so fat?"

"I ate a pot of mush,
I drank a barrel of milk,
I ate a little boy,
I ate a little girl,
I ate a little dog,
I ate a little cat,
I ate a little fox,
and I'll eat you too
if I can catch you."

So he caught the little rabbit
and swallowed her down whole.
Then he went on
till he met a little squirrel.

The little squirrel says, "Old man,
what makes you so fat?"

"I ate a pot of mush,
I drank a barrel of milk,
I ate a little boy,
I ate a little girl,
I ate a little dog,
I ate a little cat,
I ate a little fox,
I ate a little rabbit,
and...

23

I'll eat you too
if I can catch you."

The little squirrel says,
"You can't catch me, old man,"
and he ran up a tree,
with the old man after him.

The squirrel ran out
on a branch, with the old man
after him.

24

The squirrel jumped over
to another tree,
with the old man after him.

But the old man fell
and busted himself
wide open.

Little boy says, "I'm out."
Little girl says, "I'm out."
Little dog says, "I'm out."

Little cat says, "I'm out."
Little fox says, "I'm out."
Little rabbit says, "I'm out."
Little squirrel says,
"I'm out too,
'cause I wasn't in."

So Did I

I went up one step.
  So did I.
I went up two steps.
  So did I.
I went up four steps.
  So did I.
I saw a cat.
  So did I.
The cat saw a rat.
  So did I.
The cat ate the rat.
  So did...

Just Like Me

I went up one pair of stairs.
  Just like me.
I went up two pairs of stairs.
  Just like me.
I went into a room.
  Just like me.
And there I saw a monkey.

Just like
you!

Plop!

Once, by a pond,
there was a big fruit tree.
And by the big fruit tree
lived six rabbits.

One day
the rabbits went out to play.

Plop is
Coming

Just then, a big fruit fell **plop!** into the water. The rabbits jumped with fright and ran away.

A fox came by.
He saw the rabbits running.
"Why are you running, rabbits?" asked the fox.

"Plop is coming!" shouted the rabbits.

31

The fox was frightened
and he ran, too.

A monkey came by.
He saw the fox running.
"Why are you running, Fox?"
asked the monkey.

Plop is
coming!

"Plop is coming!"
shouted the fox.
The monkey was frightened
and he ran, too.

32

A tiger came by. "Why are you running, Monkey?" asked the tiger.

"Plop is coming," shouted the monkey. So the tiger ran, too.

"I don't know," answered the tiger. "The monkey told me."

Up came the monkey, puffing and puffing.

"Who is Plop?" asked the lion.

"I don't know," answered the monkey. "The fox told me."

35

Up came the fox,
puffing and puffing.

"Who is Plop?"
asked the lion.

"I don't know,"
answered the fox.
"The rabbits told me."

Up came the rabbits.
"We know! We know!"
they all shouted.

"He lives by the pond.
Come and see him."

They all went back to the pond. Just then, another big fruit fell **plop!** into the water.

"Look!" said the lion. "Your Plop is just a fruit falling into the water. How silly you all are! You nearly ran your legs off!"

Silly Mr. Fox

One day Mr. Fox went out
for a walk.   He looked back
and saw some big dogs
running after him.
So he ran as fast as he could.

Then he saw a little cave,
and in he went.

Up came the big dogs,
barking and barking.
They were too big to get in
the cave.

Mr. Fox sat there,
puffing and puffing,
with the big dogs outside.

Mr. Fox said, "I am clever
to get away from the big dogs."
Then he looked at his legs.
"Legs, legs," he said,
"what did you do
to help me get away
from the big dogs?"

"We ran and ran,"
said his legs.
"We ran into this cave."

"Yes, you did, too," said Mr. Fox.
"You are good, good legs."

Then Mr. Fox said, "Eyes, eyes,
what did you do to help me
get away from the big dogs?"

40

"We helped you," said his two eyes.
"We saw the big dogs coming.
And we saw this cave for you."
"Yes, you did, too," said Mr. Fox.
"You are good, good eyes."

Then Mr. Fox said,
"Ears, ears, what did you do
to help me get away
from the big dogs?"

"We helped you," said his two ears.
"We heard the big dogs barking.
We told you to run."

"Yes, you did, too," said Mr. Fox.
"You are good, good ears."

Then Mr. Fox
looked at his tail.
"Tail, tail," he said,
"what did you do
to help me get away
from the big dogs?

You didn't help me at all,
did you! You just
made me carry you.
Did you help me, tail?
No, you did not!"

This made the tail cross.
It said, "No, I didn't help you.
I just waved at the dogs
to come and get you.
I didn't help at all!"

42

Mr. Fox gave his tail a good bite.
"You are a bad, bad tail," he said.
"Out you go! Out of this cave,
you bad tail."

And Mr. Fox pushed his
tail out of the cave.
The big dogs caught it
and pulled and pulled.

Out came silly Mr. Fox, too.

So the big dogs caught him
after all.

Mr. Bear
Squash-it-all-flat

a play with

Mouse

Frog

Rabbit

and Mr. Bear

Reader:

Once there was
an old tin can.
A mouse came along
and looked at it.

44

Mouse:

What a good little house that
would be. I could live there.
Little house, little house,
who lives in this little house?
Oh, no one lives there.
I'll go in.

Frog comes along.

Frog:

What a good
little house that would be.
I could live there.
Little house, little house,
who lives in this little house?

45

Mouse:

I live in this little house.
But you can come in
and live here too.

Frog goes in.

Rabbit comes along.

Rabbit:

What a good little house that
would be.   I could live there.
Little house, little house,
who lives in this little house?

Mouse and Frog:

We live in this little house.
But you can come in
and live here too.

> *Rabbit goes in.*
> *Mr. Bear comes along.*

Mr. Bear:

What a good little house that
would be. I could live there.
Little house, little house,
who lives in
this little house?

47

Mouse and Frog and Rabbit:
We live in this little house.
But you can't come in!
You are far too big!

Mr. Bear:
I'm Mr. Bear Squash-it-all-flat.
And if I can't come in,
I'll squash it all flat.

Reader:
He sat on the can,
and away they ran.
He squashed
it flat. And
that was
that!

48